E N T S

Level 7: Make a Splash

You've Got the Write Idea!

Better Together

Water, Water Everywhere

UNIT 1

UNIT 2

UNIT 3

If you wish to send the books home, you may want to send a letter along to explain how parents can use the books with their children.

Dear

This year in Reading/Language Arts, your child is learning a number of important thinking strategies. A few examples of these strategies are: organizing information into main ideas and details, drawing conclusions, making predictions, and analyzing story elements like plot, setting, and character.

As we read literature in the classroom, I model the strategies and provide opportunities for students to model and apply the strategies as well. The Thinking to Read and Write Books—high-interest short stories, science fiction, humor, mysteries, plays, poems, folk tales, and information articles—provide more opportunities for students to use the strategies they are learning.

To help your child get the most out of these reading and writing experiences, I invite you to share them with him or her. Here are a few suggestions:

- Read the selections with your child. You can read the selections silently, or you can listen while your child reads to you. Taking turns reading aloud to one another is another choice.

- After reading, take some time to share your reactions to each selection. What did you enjoy, find interesting, agree or disagree with?

- Work through the activities included at the end of the selection. Encourage your child by asking questions to help him or her think through ideas and by sharing some of your own ideas. If your child writes something, invite him or her to share it with you.

By interacting with your child, you can help make these literacy experiences meaningful and motivating.

I would appreciate hearing your comments and suggestions about these materials and approaches.

Thank you in advance!

Sincerely,

THINKING TO READ AND WRITE

Strategy Application

TAKE HOME BOOKS for

Window to the Sky * Make a Splash

MACMILLAN / McGRAW-HILL SCHOOL PUBLISHING COMPANY
New York / Chicago / Columbus

CONT

Level 6: Window to the Sky

Alexander Hubble

by Dan Greenberg

Alexander Hubble
Had a dog named Trouble
And Trouble was truly a bother.
He liked to play house
With a cat and a mouse
And pretend that he was the father.

Alexander Hubble
Had a cat named Double
And Double was really a pest.
She liked to eat fish
From a solid gold dish
And never clean up the mess.

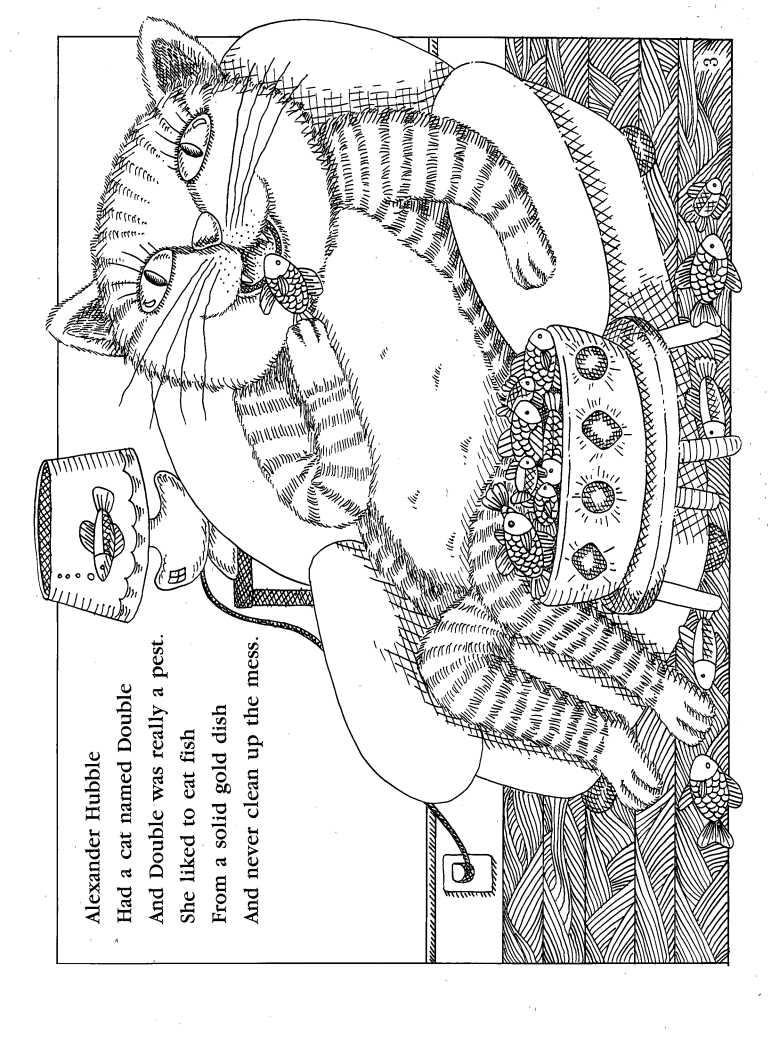

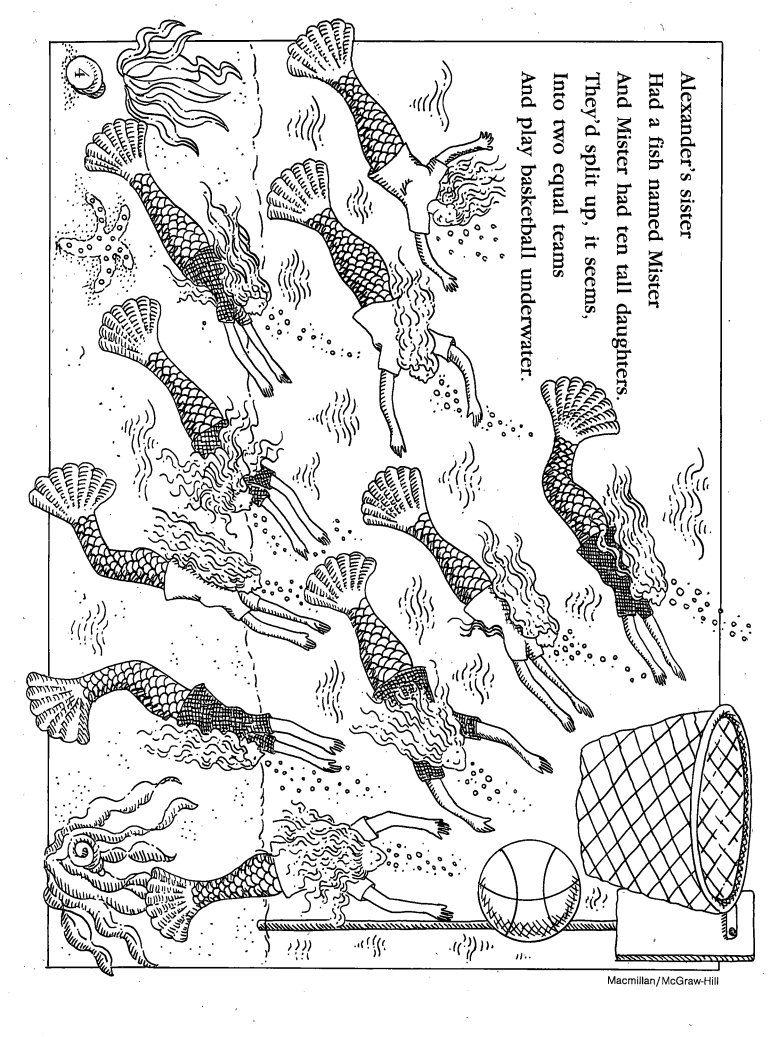

Alexander's sister
Had a fish named Mister
And Mister had ten tall daughters.
They'd split up, it seems,
Into two equal teams
And play basketball underwater.

4

Macmillan/McGraw-Hill

Alexander's mom

Had a goat named Tom

And Tom liked to look at the stars.

He'd sit on his back

And munch on a snack

And stare up at Venus and Mars.

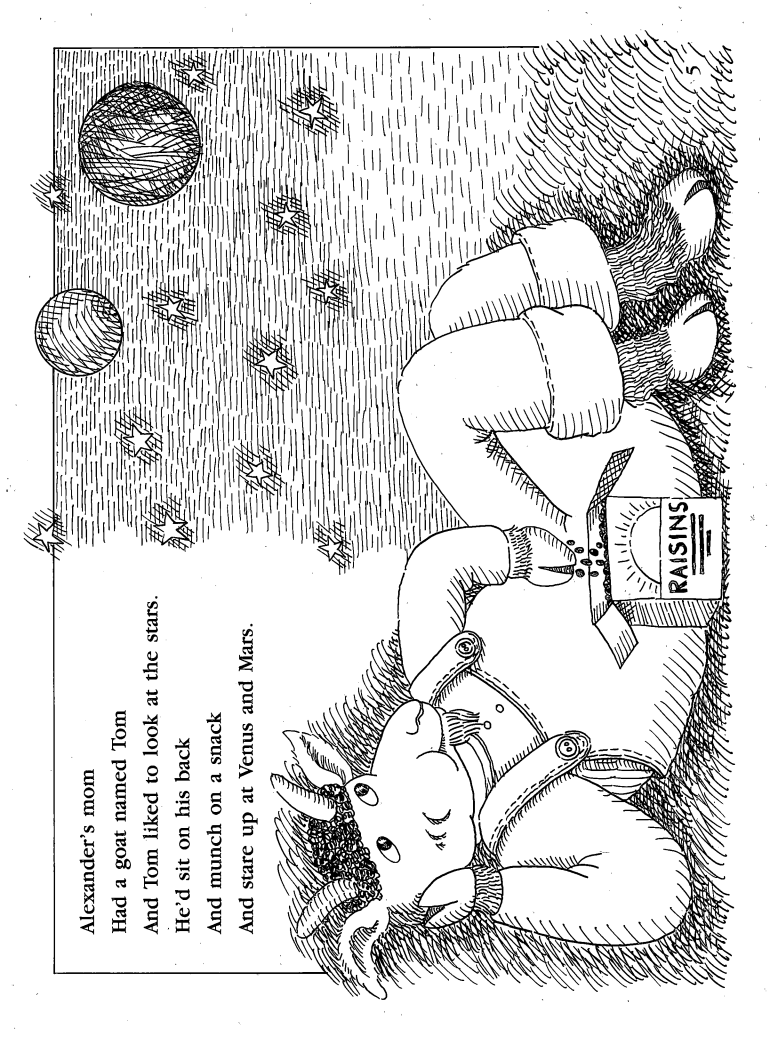

Alexander's dad
Had a bouncing pad
And all day he'd just bounce around.
He bounced so much
That he fell out of touch
With the people down there on the ground.

6

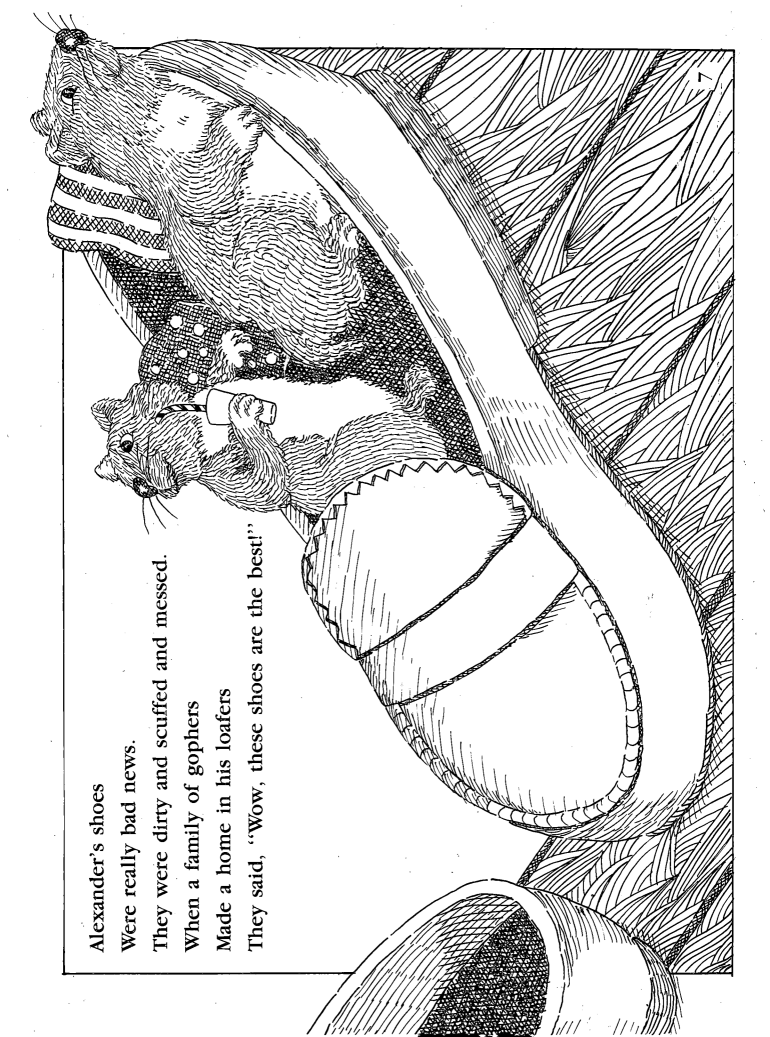

Alexander's shoes
Were really bad news.
They were dirty and scuffed and messed.
When a family of gophers
Made a home in his loafers
They said, "Wow, these shoes are the best!"

Alexander's horse
Wore shoes, of course,
She also liked to wear red socks.
She traveled in style
But after a while
They filled up with pebbles and rocks.

8

Macmillan/McGraw-Hill

Alexander's friend
Had a lizard named Ben
And Ben had a frog named June.
They'd go for walks together
In the springtime weather
And gaze at the big white moon.

Alexander Hubble
He lived in a bubble
And floated around all day.
It was all great fun
Until the hot sun
Melted his bubble away.

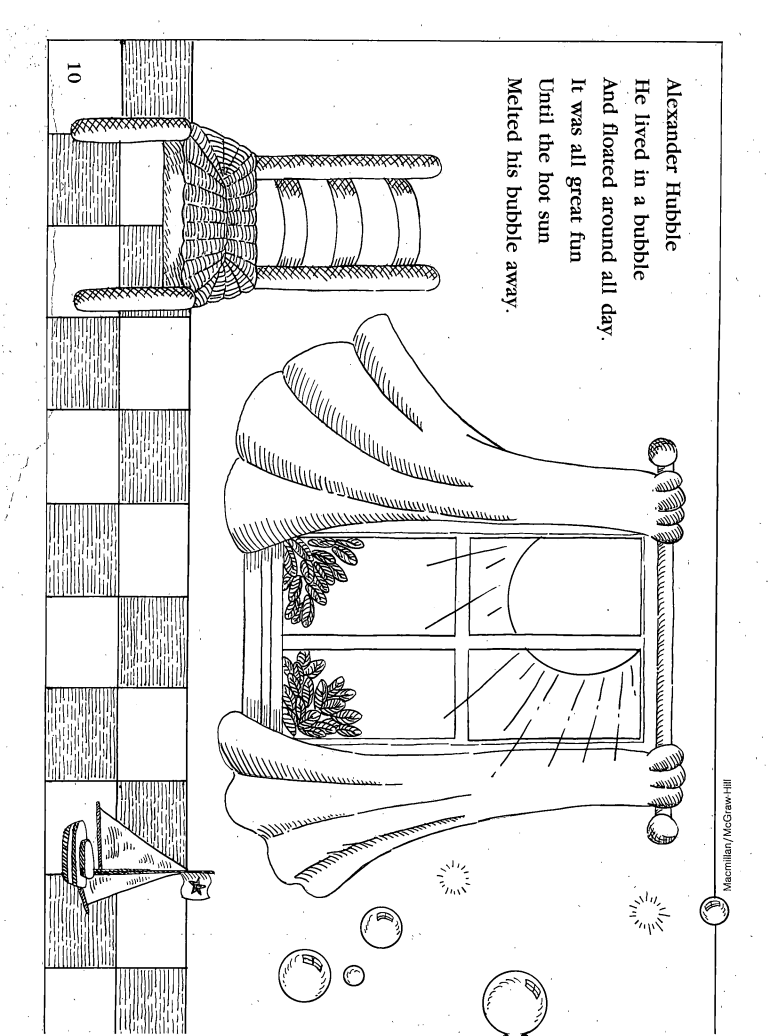

Hubble's Bubbles

Write about each character in the bubbles below. Then talk about how each character is the same as or different from the other characters in the poem.

Trouble

mom

Alexander

Double

dad

horse

sister

friend

Write a letter to Alexander Hubble. Ask him about his family, friends, or pets. What do you think he'll say to answer your questions?

12

Macmillan/McGraw-Hill

Packing the Car

Our family worked together to prepare for our camping trip. We made a list of the things that we would bring— food, clothing, books, maps, and camping gear. We packed. Then we were ready to go!

The Car Ride

My sister and I planned lots of car games. We sang songs—over and over and over again. As we went through the San Juan Mountains in Colorado, we looked for license plates from all over the United States.

"There's Texas and California!" my sister said.

"There's New Mexico! I wonder if they live near us in Santa Fe!"

Plant and Animal Life

There was so much to see and learn at Mesa Verde National Park in Colorado. We saw plants, flowers, and trees of all kinds. Small animals, such as rabbits and ground squirrels, darted out in front of us. We even saw a mule deer and its babies in the distance.

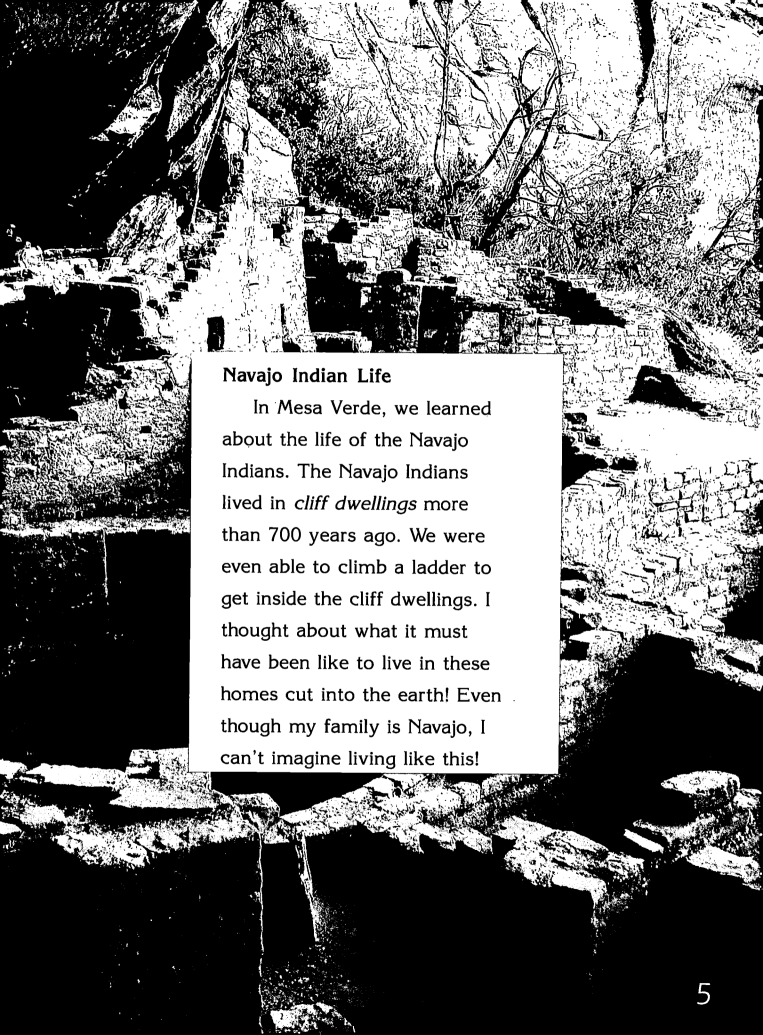

Navajo Indian Life

In Mesa Verde, we learned about the life of the Navajo Indians. The Navajo Indians lived in *cliff dwellings* more than 700 years ago. We were even able to climb a ladder to get inside the cliff dwellings. I thought about what it must have been like to live in these homes cut into the earth! Even though my family is Navajo, I can't imagine living like this!

We saw Indian drawings on the cave walls. These are called *petroglyphs.* Can you tell what the drawings might mean?

Arches National Park

The Arches

This park in Utah gets its name from its arches. There are about 200 of them! They are large sandstone sculptures. One of them is 106 feet tall! The arches have names: Landscape Arch and Skyline Arch. The arch in the picture is Delicate Arch. Can you tell why it might be called Delicate Arch?

The Animal Sculptures

Many of the rock sculptures look like animals. That's how many of them got their names: Parade of Elephants, The Duck on the Rock, Sheep Rock, Eagle Rock. Which one do you think is in the photograph?

Coming Home

We had a wonderful family vacation, but we're also glad to come home. After we unpacked the car, we invited our friends and neighbors to come over. We told them about the places we went to and the things that we saw from our Navajo heritage. We showed them our pictures and answered their questions. When our guests left, my family all agreed that vacations are fun, but there is no place like home.

9

What's the Big Idea?

Choose a paragraph from the story. Fill in the boxes below with the information from the paragraph you chose.

Main Idea

Detail

Detail

Think about a place that you have visited. Write about that place. Be sure to tell about the main idea and two or three details that tell about your main idea.

Frogs and Toads in Spring

by
Patricia Lynch

It is spring. A frog digs its way out of the bottom of the muddy pond. A toad pops out of the soft soil of the garden. They had been sleeping under the ground through the long, cold winter. Now they blink their eyes in the sunlight.

2

When darkness falls, frog and toad songs fill the night. The creaks of the bullfrogs are the loudest and deepest. "H-h-rrumph!" says the frog at the pond's edge.

The spring peeper and other tree frogs sing in tiny, creaky voices.

Toads sing the sweetest songs of all. "Tweeeee!" whistles the toad at the garden's edge.

Frogs and toads can both puff out their throats into big bubbles filled with air.

H-h-rrumph!

The air helps make the loud sound that is the frog's or toad's call. Every kind of frog or toad has a different kind of voice.

TOAD

A toad's skin is a dusty greenish-
brown. It is covered with bumps, and
it is dry. This is because the toad
lives most of its life on the land.

FROG

A frog's skin is smoother, wetter, and greener than a toad's. Most frogs live all their lives in or near water.

Frogs have long, very strong hind legs for jumping and swimming. A frog can jump 20 times as far as the length of its body!

Toads have shorter, weaker hind legs. They do not swim or jump far. Toads sit in the shade in the garden, or dig into the ground when the summer comes.

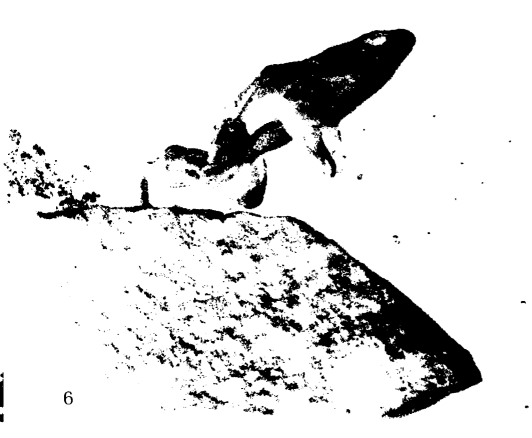

In the spring, frogs and toads both lay their eggs in ponds and quiet streams. The eggs hatch into tiny tadpoles. A tadpole looks like a very small fish.

In time, each tadpole grows legs. First it grows hind legs. Then it grows front legs. It grows lungs, so that it will be able to breathe air.

One day, the tadpole has changed. It has become a frog or a toad. It comes out of the water to live its life on land.

If it is a toad, it will find its way to the garden or to a field or a forest. If it is a frog, it may stay near the pond. Maybe it will find a stream or a marsh where there are insects to eat!

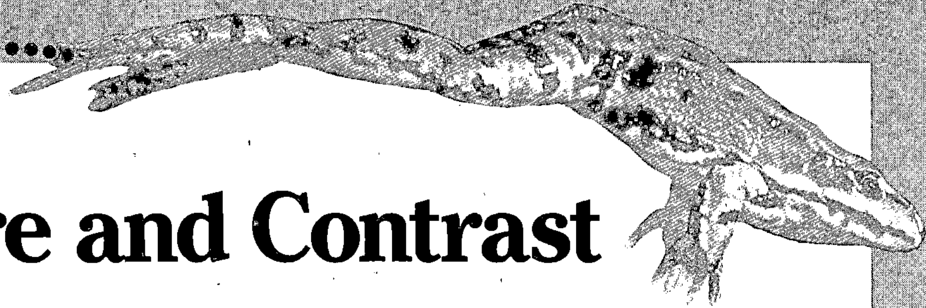

Compare and Contrast

Think about how frogs and toads are alike and different. Then, mark X's in the chart below to compare and contrast these two animals.

	Frog	Toad
Has bumpy skin		
Has smooth, wet skin		
Lives in or near water		
Lives on land		
Sings in the spring		
Lays eggs		
Starts out as a tadpole		
Spends the winter underground or at the bottom of a pond		

Now, think about the facts you wrote in the chart. Write a few sentences of your own about how frogs and toads are alike and different.

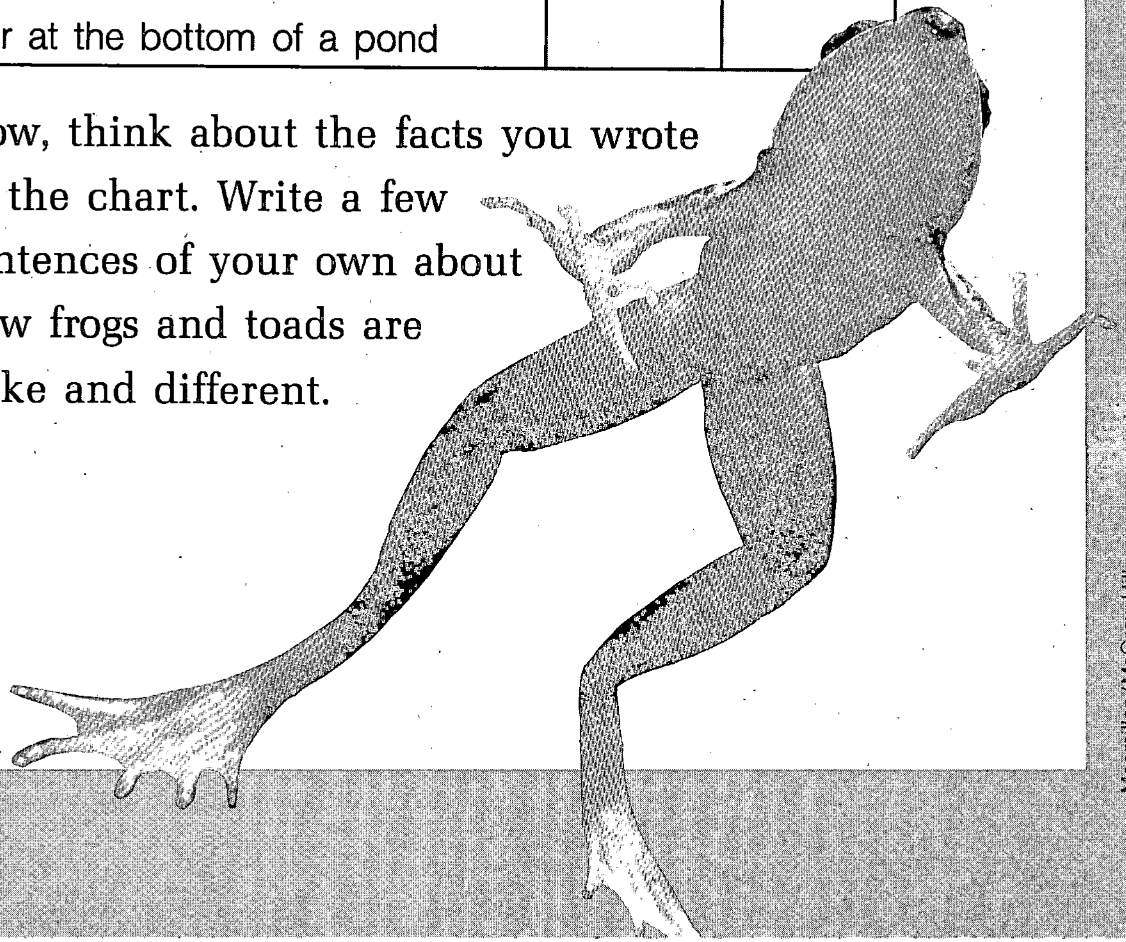

A Double Surprise

Mom is coming home soon and I can't wait! She's been away talking to some people about a new job.

I'm staying with my grandparents. I keep busy playing baseball and doing things with my grandparents, but I still miss Mom. I cross off each day on my calendar and count how many days there are left until Mom comes home.

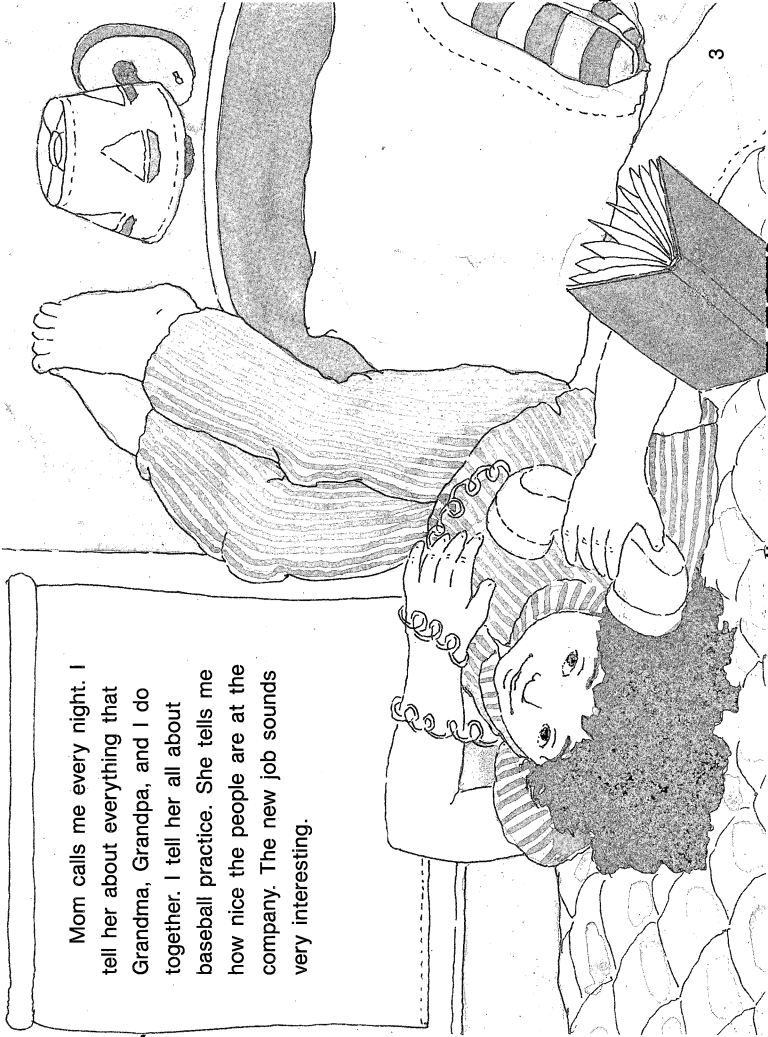

Mom calls me every night. I tell her about everything that Grandma, Grandpa, and I do together. I tell her all about baseball practice. She tells me how nice the people are at the company. The new job sounds very interesting.

At baseball practice the next day, Billy Jacobs shows me a shiny new pen and pencil set that he got for his birthday. Both the pen and the pencil are a gold color. The pencil even has a hidden eraser in it.

I tell Billy that my mom is going to get an important new job. I tell him that the pen and pencil set is perfect for my mom's new job. He offers to give me the pen and pencil set in return for my favorite baseball glove. I tell him that I will have to think about it.

What do you predict the girl will do?

4

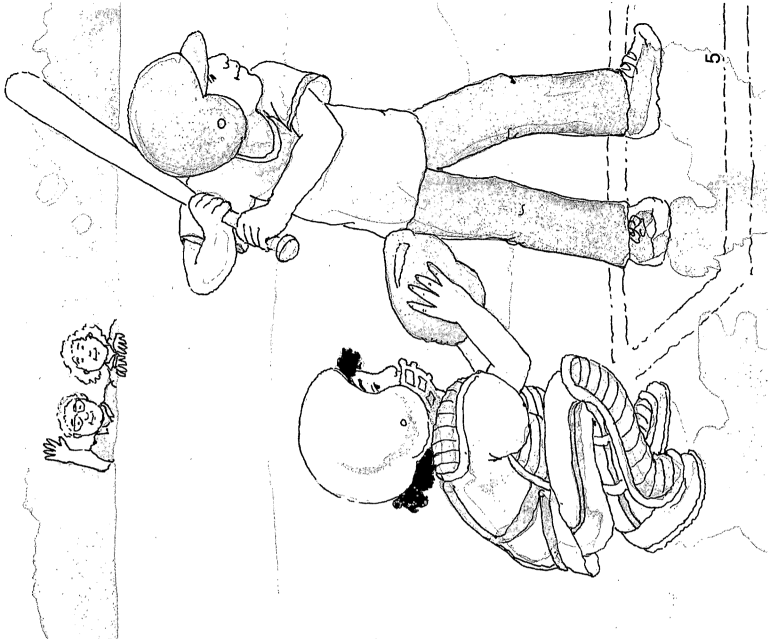

That night, Mom calls me at the same time she always does. She tells me about all the wonderful places she will go if she takes the new job. I tell her how excited I am about tomorrow's big baseball game. My team, the Cardinals, will play the Bears.

At the game against the Bears, my grandparents cheer loudly for me. I'm really glad that they are there, but I wish Mom was, too. It's just not the same playing baseball without Mom watching.

After the game, I give Billy my favorite glove. He gives me the shiny pen and pencil set.

6

Mom calls as soon as I get home. She wants to know all about the baseball game. She wants to know how I played. I tell Mom that the game was not the same without her there. She sounds sad, but she says that she will be home tomorrow. She also promises me that she will come to my next baseball game. I don't tell her that I might not be playing again because I no longer have a baseball glove.

What do you predict Mom will think about the girl's trade?

The next day goes very slowly! I can hardly wait for the bell to ring so I can run home to see Mom.

As I run home, I keep one hand in the pocket of my coat. My fingers touch the shiny pen and pencil set.

I run up the path to my grandparents' house. Mom comes out and meets me on the steps. She gives me a big hug, and I hug her back.

Then, because I can't wait anymore, I pull out the pen and pencil set and give it to Mom. "Surprise!" I say. "It's for your new job."

Mom's eyebrows rise, and her eyes light up with surprise. She smiles and thanks me. "Well, I have a surprise for you, too," she says. "I have decided not to take that new job. I would have to travel too much, and I would miss too many of your baseball games. I just couldn't stand that," she says with a smile. "So I'm just going to keep the job I have now and go to all your baseball games."

Now I am the one that is surprised! I laugh. "Well, I might not be playing too much," I say.

Mom looks at me in a confused way. I tell her about my trade with Billy Jacobs. Mom and I both laugh at this double surprise.

SURPRISE! SURPRISE! SURPRISE!

Think about the surprises in this story. What did you predict would happen *before* you finished the story? Fill in the chart. How did the story clues help you guess what would happen?

What I Thought Would Happen	Clues in the Story	What Did Happen

The Next Surprise . . .

What do you think will happen next? Write about your predictions. Share your ideas with a friend. What did he or she predict?

From Grandmama— With Love

by Marilyn Greco

I love my blanket. I have loved my
blanket ever since I can remember.
Mama says that my blanket is called
a *quilt*. She thinks I love my blanket,
or quilt, because it was made by my
Grandmama—for my Mama—many,
many years ago.

"How did Grandmama make my quilt?" I asked.

"Long ago," Mama said, "people saved their old clothes so that they could use the fabric to make other things. One of the things they made from these scraps were quilts."

I touched the soft pieces of
material that were sewn together to
form my quilt.

"Grandmama chose the material
that she wanted from her favorite old
clothes. Then she washed it," Mama
explained. "That way, all the material
was clean and soft. She wanted to be
sure the colors in the different kinds
of fabric would not run together.
Grandmama washed all that material
again and again."

"Next, Grandmama chose a pattern. She could have chosen a pattern from many designs—a star, a flower, a tree. But Grandmama chose a heart pattern for us. She said the hearts would always remind us of how much she loved us."

I looked down at the neatly sewn heart shapes of the quilt.

"Then," Mama continued, "Grandmama cut heart shapes as well as other shapes from the fabric. She cut each piece carefully by hand. Grandmama cut out little patches. That is why your blanket is called a patchwork quilt."

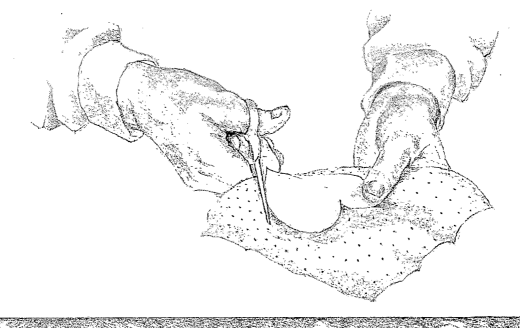

4

"How did Grandmama put all the cut pieces together?" I asked.

Mama pointed to the small stitches that held the fabric together. "Grandmama sewed each scrap together with a needle and thread. The pieces of fabric formed the design that she wanted. It took her a long time, because she did it by hand. Then Grandmama added the border," Mama replied.

"And then our quilt was finished?" I asked Mama.

"Oh, no. Once Grandmama had sewn all the pieces together into a pattern and added the border, she sewed the layers of the quilt together."

"The layers?" I asked.

"Yes," said Mama, "Any quilt has a back, a front, and a middle layer."

"Then was the quilt finished?" I
asked Mama in a very sleepy voice.

"Just about," Mama said. "The
final step was to put a strip of cloth
all around the edge of the quilt. Once
this border was sewn on, the quilt
was finished."

Mama leaned over, tucked me into
my quilt, and kissed me good night.
"From Grandmama and from Mama—
with love," she whispered.

Step By Step

What are the steps needed to make a quilt? Make notes. Then use what you have written to write a summary.

How to Make a Quilt

1. _____
2. _____
3. _____
4. _____
5. _____
6. _____
7. _____

Now, make a quilt out of colored construction paper! Choose the colored paper that you will use for your quilt. Then decide on a pattern. Cut out the pieces for the pattern and paste them together on the colored paper. Finally, paste a strip around the edge of your paper quilt for the border.

Moose on the Loose

by Karla Beatty

It was turning out to be a bad day for a curious moose. He just wanted to visit the small town by the woods in which he lived, but somehow this got him in a lot of trouble.

The first thing the moose saw when he entered Bridgetown was a white line painted down the middle of the road. Curious, he stood there and bent down to take a taste of the line.

Cars and trucks screeched to a halt to see the moose in the middle of the road.

When Sheriff Wilson saw the moose, he raced out of the diner and into his patrol car. The sheriff turned on his siren and honked his horn, but he could not get through the stopped traffic.

"I have to make that moose return to the woods where he belongs," the sheriff said. "He's going the wrong way. He could go into town instead of the woods."

3

The next thing the curious moose saw was the green awning of the beauty shop. He was a hungry moose. So up the sidewalk he went to get a bite to eat.

Sheriff Wilson got out of his car and tried to chase the moose away from the awning, but it was too late. The awning fell and caught on the moose's antlers. The moose continued down the street, looking like a circus tent with the green awning on his antlers.

Then the moose spotted the large fountain in front of Town Hall. Sheriff Wilson tried to circle around the big animal. Before he could get to him, the moose had climbed into the fountain's pool and was taking a long drink. The fountain showered the moose with its spray, and then the cement under him broke apart from his weight.

5

Meanwhile, the news spread that there was a moose on the loose. All the townspeople got into their cars and drove into town to see the curious moose with the green awning on its antlers. Soon, people, cars, trucks, and bicycles were jammed into town. The sheriff couldn't even get through to follow the moose.

People started yelling and honking their horns. They made so much noise that the moose decided that he had had enough of life in the town. With the green awning still stuck to his antlers, he trotted around the cars and trucks, went down the street, and back into the woods. The moose has never returned to the town, but people to this day still tell the story about the "wrong-way moose."

Follow That Moose!

Think about the problems the curious moose caused in Bridgetown. Then fill in the numbered boxes to tell what happened.

1.

2.

3.

4.

5.

6.

SHERIFF

How would you help the sheriff get a curious moose to leave town and go back to the woods? Make a list of things you could do to help.

Greetings from Camp Wickawac

by Deborah Eaton

Macmillan/McGraw-Hill

Return to Sender!

Sarah changed during this story. Think about her feelings at the beginning of the story. Think about her feelings at the end of the story. What clues helped you know her feelings? Fill in the chart.

Sarah's Feelings About Camp Wickawac

At the Beginning	At the End
CLUES:	CLUES:

What did you think about Camp Wickawac? Pretend you are there. Write a letter about it. Draw a picture to go with your letter.

16.

Sunday
June 21

Dear Mother and Father,
   I don't like it here.
Camp Wickawac is a bunch
of old shacks in the woods.
There is nothing to do.
The other kids all look
bigger than me. Please
come get me!

Your daughter,
Sarah

2

Monday
July 6

Dear Mommy and Daddy,

Sorry I haven't written for a while. I have been very busy. All the other kids are staying until July 14. May I please stay at camp for an extra week?

Your happy camper,
Sarah →

CAMP WICKAWAC
NORTHBERG, ME
Sarah Rios
Cabin 12

Mr. + Mrs. Rios
Scenic Drive
Belmar, N.J. 01293

SWIMMING
HIKING TRAIL
SAILBOATS
CAMPSITE 3

CAMP WICKAWAC

14

Monday
June 22

Mother and Father,
I **REALLY** don't
like it here! There is
no one to talk to.

Your daughter,
Sarah

Monday
June 29

Dear Mommy and Daddy,
   My friends and I are
getting ready to play in
the Camp Olympics today.
I'm on the red team. I
hope my team wins!

          Much Love,

               Sarah

Tuesday
June 23

To Mom and Dad,

   It gets very dark here at
night. There are no street
lights. We try hard not to
be too scared, but a skunk
got under our cabin last
night. It must have been
running from the camp
dog. Please come get me
now! I mean it!

Sarah Rios

Saturday
June 27

Dear Mommy and Daddy,
I guess camp is O.K.
I have made a few new
friends.

Love,
xox
Sarah

Wednesday
June 24

Dear Mom and Dad,
We learned to tie knots
today. Did you know that
tying a good knot could
save my life one day?
Miss Hanson said I did
an outstanding job. Do
you think I could join the
Explorers Club after
school next year?

Love,
Sarah

Blue Ribbon Beagle

by
Karla Beatty

The big tent heats up as the afternoon sun shines down on the Championship Dog Show. The owners and their dogs are anxiously waiting for their time before the judge. They each hope their dog will be the special one chosen for the blue ribbon.

Macmillan/McGraw-Hill

The making of a good show dog starts before the puppy is even born. The puppy's breeding is important.

The *breeder* is a person who raises special types of dogs for shows. He or she makes sure that each dog has a good pedigree. The mom and dad of the little pup are looked at. Were they champions? Is winning first prize possible in the puppy's family?

Have you heard the word *pedigree* before?

Owners choose a dog to show that has all the best qualities of its breed. Each little beagle, for instance, should be black, tan, and white. Its ears should be soft and long enough to stretch almost to the end of its nose.

What else do you think makes a good show dog?

A lot of hard work is put into making these dogs ready to show. The groomer must trim the nails, clean the ears, brush the teeth, and bathe and brush the dog before every show! Also, before they can compete, all dogs must be well-trained.

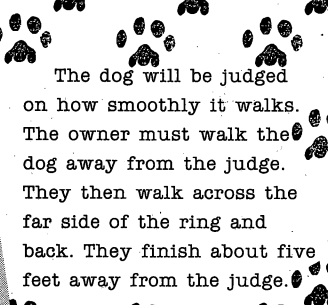

The dog will be judged on how smoothly it walks. The owner must walk the dog away from the judge. They then walk across the far side of the ring and back. They finish about five feet away from the judge.

Why do you think the owner wears an armband with a number?

The owner makes sure that everything is ready before the dog is shown to the judge. The dog has been brushed and walked. It will have its show leash and collar on. The owner will wear an armband with a number on it.

Then into the ring they go! The dogs and owners line up. The judge looks at each dog. She will decide which dogs look best and perform well.

Gaiting pattern means a walking through the ring in a pattern.

Next, the judge sends the dogs to perform the gaiting pattern. All the beautiful dogs walk through the ring in a pattern. Everyone watches and claps for his or her favorite dog.

The decision is up to the judge. Everyone waits. Finally, one lucky owner will see the blue ribbon pinned to a dog!

STEP LIVELY!

In *Blue Ribbon Beagle*, you read about making a champion show dog. Now fill in the chart to show the steps in making dogs ready to show.

1.

2.

3.

4.

5.

6.

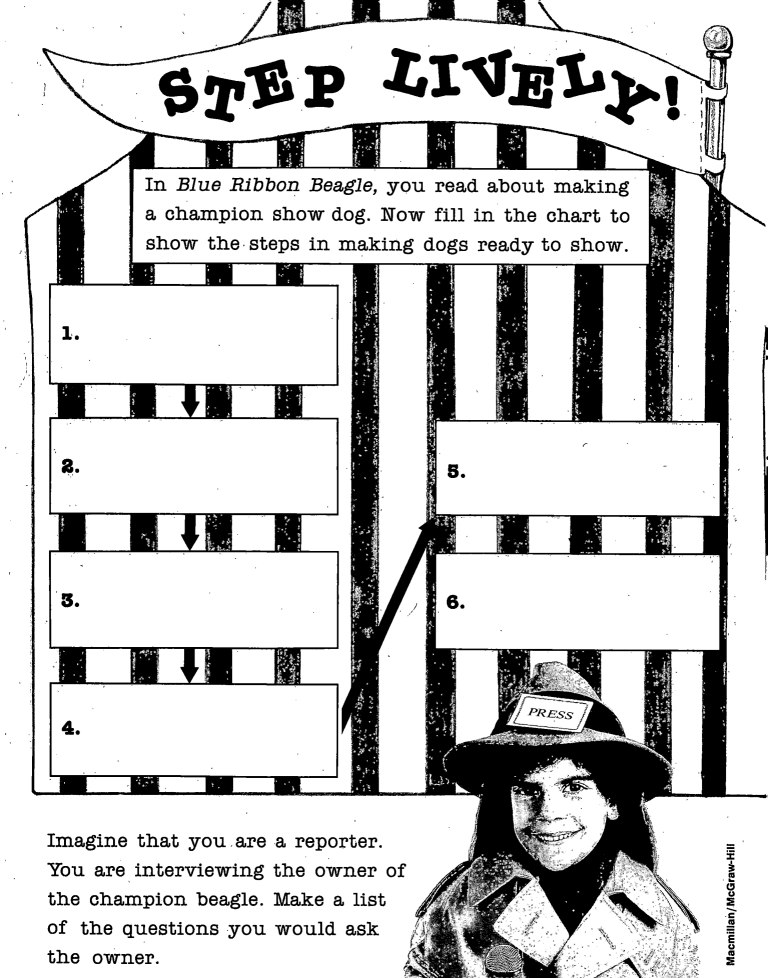

Imagine that you are a reporter. You are interviewing the owner of the champion beagle. Make a list of the questions you would ask the owner.

8

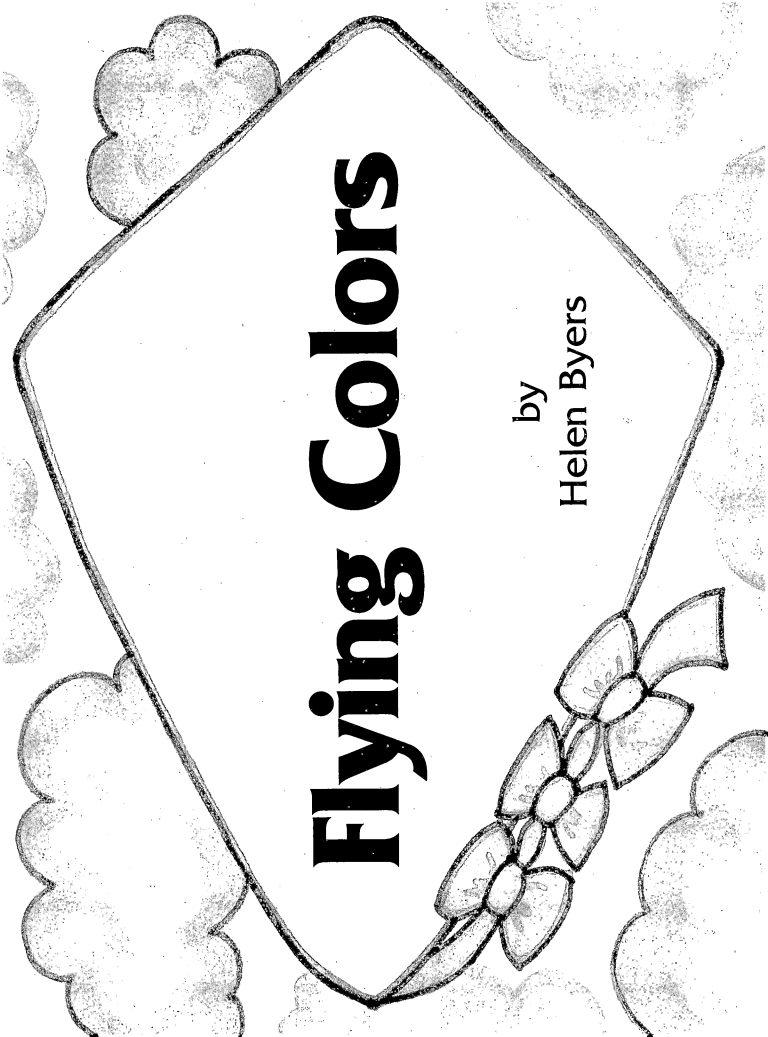

Flying Colors

by
Helen Byers

"It's perfect!"

Rosa's voice makes me jump. I want to keep sleeping, but I can't help but be awake after hearing Rosa. I rub my eyes and notice that there's something blurry by the window. It's Rosa. How can she be dressed already? She's looking out the window, doing a dance!

"Mateo! It's perfect!" she says again, only louder this time. I still haven't answered. I'm still so sleepy. Then I remember. This could be our day! We first have to check the weather!

I spring out of bed and land next to Rosa. First, we study the trees. Their leaves are moving gently. The sun is shining brightly. There are only a few clouds. Rosa is right. The day is perfect for our second annual homemade kite-flying contest! We have a lot to do!

There is a kite-flying festival in a city in Japan that's more than 400 years old. People fly brightly painted kites that are taller than adults!

3

Rosa and I make a list of all the things we'll need to make our kites.

At breakfast, we are getting more excited as we look over our list. Mom is curious to know about our plans. We show her our list and ask her if she'll take us to the store. We're in luck! She says yes.

At the store, we know just where to find what we need. Rosa pays with the quarters, dimes, nickels, and pennies that we've saved especially for this day since last year.

When we get home, the real fun can start! Rosa and I begin to make our kites. I paint my kite carefully to look like a wonderful bright bird. Rosa uses felt-tip markers and makes a picture of something wild and colorful.

Did you know that the word *kite* comes from the name of a graceful bird that soars like a kite?

4

When I've tied the last knot on my kite tail, Rosa and I both jump up at once. Now we're ready to walk to the park!

We carry our lovely new kites gently as we go … one … two … three blocks.

At the park, we hunt for the perfect spot.

"Here!" I call to Rosa.

Then comes the best part. We each make a secret wish. Whoever gets his or her kite as high as the treetops first will win. The winner's wish will come true. We close our eyes tight.

"Okay?" Rosa yells, and we run to our starting positions. We hold our kites and spools just right. Then Rosa shouts, "GO!"

As we start running, we let go of our kites, letting out some string. The wind catches Rosa's kite just when it catches mine. My kite dips, climbs, then dives. Rosa's kite lifts, twists, and flutters like a wing.

Some Kite Safety Rules:
- Never fly kites in wet or stormy weather.
- Never fly kites near electric lines or use metal in the line.

6

Both kites are in the air! They go up and up! We stop running. They seem to hang above the trees, dancing together.

I call to Rosa, "Did we both win?" She calls back, "We both get our wishes!"

Then we watch my bright bird and Rosa's brilliant colors start to fly.

Did you know that kites are the oldest form of aircraft?

Up, Up, Up and Away!

Think about the most important things that happen during Mateo and Rosa's kite-flying day. What things do they do first? What do they do next? Organize the story by listing the events in order within each kite.

First:

Mateo wakes up. He and Rosa check the weather.

Then:

Next:

Then:

Last:

Now pretend that you are Rosa or Mateo. Write a diary entry telling about your day.

Macmillan/McGraw-Hill

Are We Still Friends?

by Helen Byers

Are We Still Friends?

Kevin doesn't want to be friends anymore. I can tell from the way he acts. He acts different!

We used to be best friends. We used to play at recess and on Saturdays. Now Kevin doesn't wait for me at recess. He doesn't ask if I want to play on Saturdays.

Kevin seems different. Last week, I went up to him and Sam at recess. They were playing a new game with a kickball. I said, "Can I play, too?"

Kevin laughed! He said, "I don't know, Josh."

Then he got an odd look on his face and ran to the other side of the playground.

3

Kevin never sits by me on the school bus, either. Yesterday afternoon, he sat by Sam. I sat way in the back. I didn't feel like talking to anybody. Maria sat down next to me, but I just looked out the window.

Maria's nice. She asked if I was getting excited about moving and going to the new school across town.

"I guess so," I said.

"When's your last day here?" she asked.

I didn't feel like talking about it.

"Soon," I said.

Then, all of a sudden, Maria got quiet, too. Just before she got off the bus, she said, "I wish you didn't have to move."

I was still thinking about what Maria said
when the bus stopped at Kevin's house.
From the sidewalk, he looked back over his
shoulder to see if I was watching. I waved.
But he didn't even wave back! He just got
that odd look on his face again.

Today was my last day at school. Miss Evans and our class had a little party for me. They gave me a big card they had made. Everyone had written something nice inside—everyone except Kevin. He only wrote his name. I think he did that to hurt my feelings.

Kevin

Good bye Josh!!

We'll miss you Judy

Miss you Tom

Jose

Bye in Lynn

Good luck Heath

6

It feels funny to be walking to the school bus for the last time. Then I feel someone's finger poking at my shoulder. It's Kevin! He doesn't look mean or mad. But he has that look on his face again. I look closer. Then I see that Kevin looks like he might cry!

"Hi," I say.

"Hi," he says back.

"What's the matter?" I ask him.

"Nothing," he says.

Then he says, "I bet you can't wait to move! I bet you'll make a lot of new friends!"

7

All of a sudden, I think that I understand why Kevin's been acting the way he has.

I tell him, "I might make new friends. But you and I can still play on Saturdays!"

"We can?" he says.

Then he says, "Want to sit on the bus together?"

When the bus stops at Kevin's house, he jumps up and gets off without saying good-bye. From the sidewalk, he turns to see if I'm watching. I wave. Then Kevin smiles and waves to me.

That's What Friends Are For!

Josh learned that what he was thinking about Kevin wasn't true. How did Josh find out what Kevin was really thinking? Fill in the chart. Next to each event, write how Josh felt in the beginning and then write what he later found out.

	What Josh Thinks	What Josh Finds Out
Kevin doesn't want to play anymore.	_____	_____
	_____	_____
	_____	_____
Kevin doesn't sit by Josh on the bus.	_____	_____
	_____	_____
	_____	_____
Kevin doesn't write something nice on Josh's card.	_____	_____
	_____	_____
	_____	_____

PUT YOURSELF IN KEVIN'S PLACE. In the story, Josh learned that what he thought about Kevin led him to a conclusion that wasn't true. Now, pretend that you are Kevin. Write a letter to Josh, explaining why you acted as you did.

10

STORM
AT
RUGGED
POINT

by

Karla Beatty

Rugged Point Lighthouse never fails! My dad is the lighthouse keeper. He always says that no matter how hard the rain falls, how fast the wind blows, or how high the waves grow, Rugged Point Lighthouse must always glow. The ships at sea need the warning light so that they don't crash on the rocks below the lighthouse.

Rugged Point is a rocky arm of land that juts out like a green wool stocking filled with lumps of coal. There's just enough room on the ankle for the lighthouse and the little house that Mom, Dad, my younger brother Sam, and I live in.

We knew that there was a hurricane coming that day. First, the radio came on with a warning. HURRICANE BUILDING UP SPEED! EVACUATION POSSIBLE! Then, the wind started whipping. Next, the rain came pouring down like a waterfall. Soon our ears were filled with the noise of the crash of the waves against the rocks.

4

The tide was growing higher and higher—soon it could spill over and attack our little house. We had to get out of there!

But first, we had to prepare our lighthouse and home against the hurricane. We covered all the windows with boards. We brought some chairs and one table that we kept outside into the house. We also knew that the light in the lighthouse must continue to glow like a red eye blinking through the darkness of the storm.

6

Dad drove us to the junior high school rescue station. We spent the night in the very crowded gym, sleeping on the floor with the other families.

It was a long night of waiting and hoping. All night long I listened to the sound of the rain on the gym roof.

During the night, the hurricane passed over.

We stepped outside to a day filled with sparkling sun. As we drove home, we saw that the light in the lighthouse was still blinking. The house was still there, but the fence was down and the bottom windows of the house were broken. The waves just invited themselves in!

We got to work quickly. All the furniture, rugs, and curtains were put out in the sun to dry. Dad and I put what was left of the fence back, while Mom and Sam mopped the floors in the house.

Later, we all helped pick up scraps from the yard. Soon things were almost back to normal. As we were working, I looked up at the light, just to make sure. Rugged Point Lighthouse never fails!

Think about the people and the events in "Storm at Rugged Point." Then fill in the story map to show the order of events in the story.

First:

_____

_____

Next:

_____

_____

Then:

_____

_____

Finally:

_____

_____

THE EYE OF THE STORM

Imagine that you are helping at the rescue station in the school gym. List some things that the families staying there might need.

_____

_____

_____

_____

_____

_____

_____

Macmillan/McGraw-Hill

How Do Your Vegetables Grow?

by Marilyn Greco

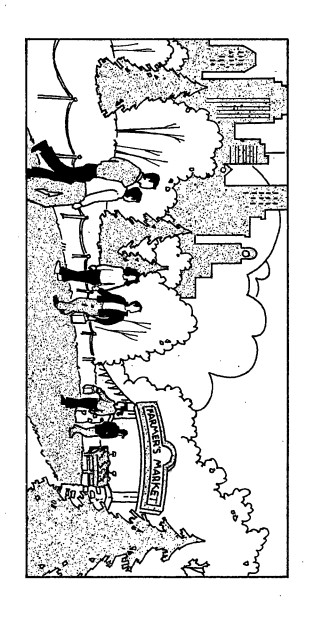

Everyone knew about it. The Big Farmer's Market was being held on Saturday morning. All who wanted to go to it from far and near, from farms and cities, were welcome. It promised to be a great day. And indeed it was!

"I grow vegetables," said Mr. Sousa.

"I grow vegetables, too," said Amy.

"I grow vegetables in my garden," said Amy.

"I grow vegetables on my farm," said Mr. Sousa.

Have you ever seen a plow?

In the spring, Mr. Sousa prepares the soil. First he plows the soil. A tractor pulls the plow. Then he plants the seeds. A machine called a seeder helps Mr. Sousa plant seeds. He plants seeds for peppers, beans, and carrots.

4

Have you ever used a hoe or a rake?

In the spring, Amy prepares the soil, too. But Amy does not use a tractor, a plow, or a seeder. Amy uses a hoe and a rake to make the soil smooth. She uses the hoe to make a *burrow*, or hole, for the seeds. Just like Mr. Sousa, Amy plants seeds for peppers, beans, and carrots.

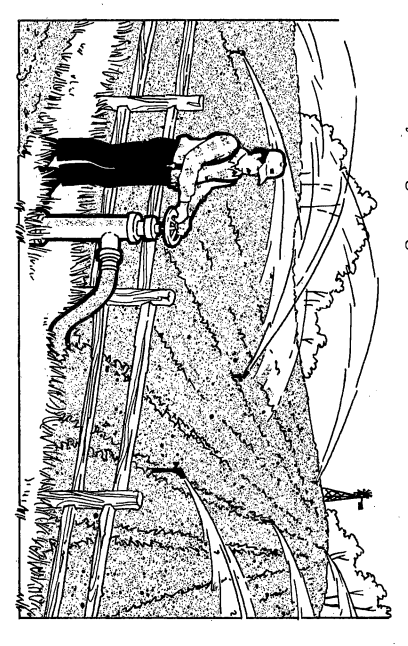

Throughout the spring and summer, Mr. Sousa waits for the rain. If it doesn't rain, he waters the plants with a machine. He keeps the ground soft and smooth. This is called cultivation. A cultivator is the machine Mr. Sousa uses to break up the soil. He checks his plants to make sure they are growing well.

Throughout the spring and summer, Amy waits for rain. If it doesn't rain, she waters her plants, too. Amy uses a watering can. Amy keeps the ground soft and smooth, just like Mr. Sousa does. But Amy does not use a machine. She cultivates her garden with a rake and hoe. She checks each day to make sure her plants are growing well.

In late summer and fall, Mr. Sousa's vegetables are ready. He has worked very hard. Mr. Sousa, the sun, the rain, and the soil all helped to make the vegetables grow. It is time to gather the crops. This is called the *harvest*. Mr. Sousa uses a harvesting machine to pick crops.

How do you think Amy will gather her crops?

In late summer and fall, Amy's vegetables are ready, too. Amy has worked very hard. Amy, the sun, the rain, and the soil all helped to make the vegetables grow. It is time to gather the crops. Just like on Mr. Sousa's farm, Amy will need to harvest her crops. But she doesn't use a harvesting machine. Amy picks her crops by hand.

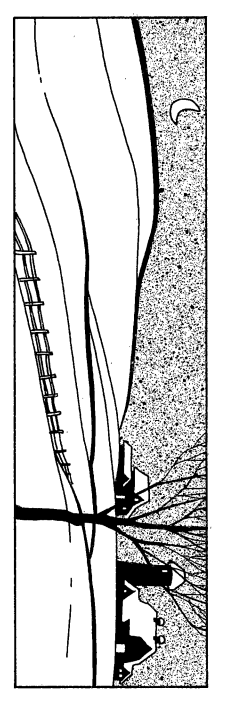

Mr. Sousa is happy. Amy is happy. They are pleased with the vegetables they have grown.

In the winter, Mr. Sousa rests. In the winter, Amy rests.

In the winter, the soil rests.

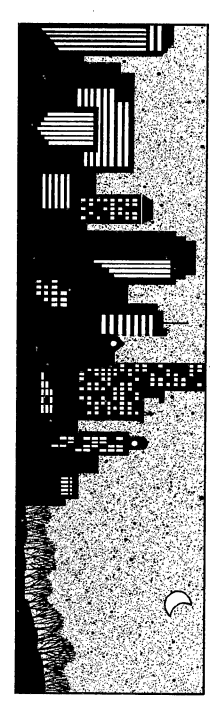

But in the spring, both Mr. Sousa and Amy will begin planting all over again. They will again need all the ingredients for growing vegetables—hard work, the sun, the soil, and rain.

THINKING ABOUT VEGETABLES!

How were Amy's and Mr. Sousa's vegetables alike?
Fill in the boxes with the information from the story.

	Amy's Vegetables	Mr. Sousa's Vegetables
Where vegetables are grown:		
How the soil is prepared:		
Kinds of vegetables:		
What makes the vegetables grow:		

Imagine that you are Mr. Sousa. Then imagine that you are Amy. What do you think you will do with your vegetables once they are harvested? Will you eat them at dinner? Will you sell them? Complete each of the following statements:

If I were Mr. Sousa, I would. . . _____

If I were Amy, I would. . . _____

How are your answers similar?
How are your answers different?

SIGNS OF SUCCESS

Suggestions for evaluating student responses and discussing the selections.

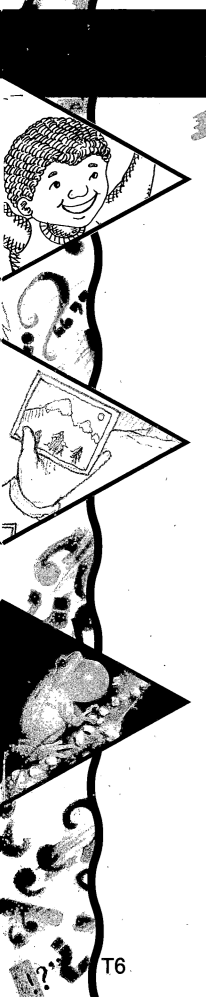

Suggestions for evaluating student responses and discussing the selections.

•••••••••••••••• ALEXANDER HUBBLE ••••••••••••••••

STRATEGIES: *Analyze story elements: character/Summarize*
Have students write about each character in the bubble designated for that character. Then encourage students to talk about how each character is the same or different from the other characters.

When students analyze the characters, look for:
- *Logical reasoning:* Are students' responses consistent with the description of the characters in the selection?
- *Completeness:* Do students include all the major points about the characters?
- *Specifics:* Do students provide details to support their comparisons of the characters?

••••••••••••••••• OUR FAMILY VACATION ••••••••••••••••

STRATEGIES: *Organize information: main idea and supporting details/Summarize*
Ask students to reread a paragraph from the selection. Then have them write the main idea and details of that paragraph in the boxes provided.

When students organize information into main ideas and supporting details, look for:
- *Specifics:* Do students identify the main ideas of the paragraphs?
- *Supporting Information:* Do students use details they have read or seen in the pictures to support the main ideas of the paragraphs?
- *Organization:* Have the charts been completed so that the main ideas and details of the paragraphs are clear?

••••••••••• FROGS AND TOADS IN SPRING •••••••••••

STRATEGIES: *Organize information: comparison and contrast/Draw conclusions*
Encourage students to compare and contrast frogs and toads. Then, ask students to mark X's in the chart to show how frogs and toads are alike and different.

When students compare and contrast, look for:
- *Specifics:* Do students recognize the similarities and differences between frogs and toads?
- *Reasons:* Do students support their conclusions about frogs and toads with information in the selection or from their own experiences?
- *Completeness:* Do students include all the information about frogs and toads to complete the chart?

SUCCESS

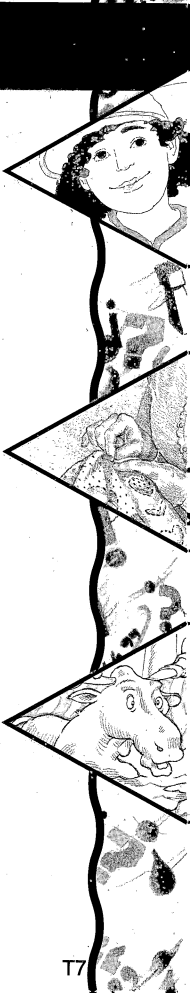

•••••••••••••••• A DOUBLE SURPRISE ••••••••••••••••

STRATEGIES: *Make, confirm, or revise predictions*
Ask students to think about the surprises in the story and to fill in the first column of the chart based on what they predicted would happen. Then, have students fill in the rest of the chart. Encourage students to discuss how the story clues helped them to predict what would happen.

When students make, confirm, or revise predictions, look for:
- *Logic:* Do students' predictions flow logically from the events and clues within the story?
- *Specifics:* Do students refer to details in the story to give support for their predictions?
- *Foreshadowing:* Are the story clues the students identify consistent with what actually happens in the story?

•••••••••• FROM GRANDMAMA—WITH LOVE ••••••••••

STRATEGIES: *Organize information: steps in a process/Summarize*
Encourage students to think about the process of making a quilt. Have students make notes about this process. Than ask students to use these notes to write a summary of the steps needed to make a quilt.

When students organize information into steps, look for:
- *Chronology:* Do students refer to the steps in the process in the correct order?
- *Completeness:* Do students include all the important steps?
- *Details:* Do students refer to details in the text that support their notes about the process of making a quilt?

•••••••••••••••• MOOSE ON THE LOOSE ••••••••••••••••

STRATEGIES: *Organize information: sequence of events*
Have students review the story and fill in the numbered boxes to tell what happened.

When students organize information in order, look for:
- *Sequence:* Do students organize the events in the correct order?
- *Completeness:* Do students include all the important events?

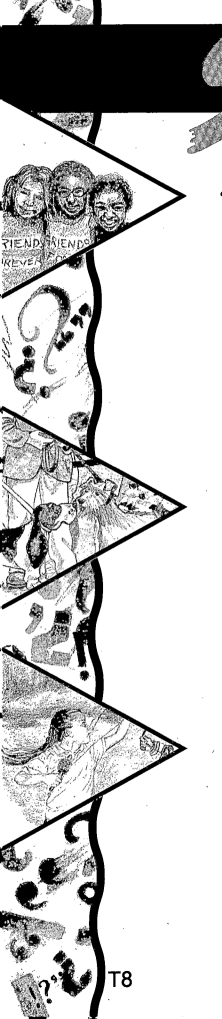

SIGNS OF

Suggestions for evaluating student responses and discussing the selections.

•••••••• GREETINGS FROM CAMP WICKAWAC ••••••••

STRATEGIES: *Use illustrations/Organize information: comparison and contrast*
Encourage students to think about how Sarah changed during this story. Ask them to think about Sarah's feelings at the beginning and at the end of the story. Then have students complete the chart using clues from the illustrations and story.

When students use illustrations, look for:
- *Relatedness:* Do students use the illustrations to make inferences about the setting and the characters' feelings?

When students compare and contrast, look for:
- *Specifics:* Do students refer to details in the story when comparing and contrasting settings and characters' feelings?
- *Attention to changes in character's feelings:* Do students compare and contrast Sarah's feelings at the beginning and at the end of the story?

•••••••••••••••• BLUE RIBBON BEAGLE ••••••••••••••••

STRATEGIES: *Organize information: steps in a process*
Encourage students to pretend they are walking their dog along the path in the ring before the judges. Then have students complete the chart showing the steps in the making of a good show dog.

When students organize information into steps in a process, look for:
- *Chronology:* Do students organize the information in a clear way with each step in the correct order?
- *Clue Words:* Do students use clue words to help them identify the sequence of events?

•••••••••••••••••••• FLYING COLORS ••••••••••••••••••••

STRATEGIES: *Organize information: sequence of events*
Encourage students to think about the most important things that happened during Mateo and Rosa's kite-flying day. Then have students organize the story by listing the events in order within each kite.

When students organize information in order, look for:
- *Sequence:* Do students list the events in the story in the right order?
- *Important Information:* Do students include all the important events, and leave out the unimportant ones?

SUCCESS

•••••••••••••• ARE WE STILL FRIENDS? ••••••••••••••

STRATEGIES: *Analyze story elements: character, plot/Draw conclusions*
Encourage students to think about how Josh felt about Kevin at the beginning of the story and then what he later found out.

When students complete the chart, look for:
- *Characterization:* Do students' descriptions of story characters' reactions to plot events make sense?

When students draw conclusions, look for:
- *Specifics:* Do students refer to details in the selection and their own experiences to give support for their conclusions?
- *Logical reasoning:* Do students use information from the story to support their conclusions?

••••••••••••• STORM AT RUGGED POINT ••••••••••••••

STRATEGIES: *Organize information: sequence of events*
Encourage students to think about the people and events in the story. Then have them fill in the story map to show the order of events.

When students organize information from the story in order, look for:
- *Sequence:* Do students refer to the story events in the correct sequence?
- *Organization:* Do students organize the information in a logical way?
- *Important Information:* Do students include all the important events, and leave out the unimportant ones?

•••••••• HOW DO YOUR VEGETABLES GROW? ••••••••

STRATEGIES: *Organize information: compare and contrast*
Encourage students to think about how Amy's and Mr. Sousa's vegetables were alike and different.
Have students fill in the boxes on the chart with information from the story.

When students fill in the chart, look for:
- *Comparing and Contrasting:* Do students include ways in which both Amy's and Mr. Sousa's vegetables are alike and different?
- *Specifics:* Do students refer to details in the story when comparing and contrasting vegetables?
- *Reasons:* Do students support their conclusions about the vegetables with information in the selection or from their own experiences?

Book Design and Production   Kirchoff/Wohlberg, Inc.

Cover Design   Kirchoff/Wohlberg, Inc.

Cover Photography   Frank White/Liaison International

Illustration   *Alexander Hubble*, Alexandra Wallner; *Our Family Vacation*, Diane Paterson; Tom Leonard; *Double Surprise*, Diane Paterson; *Moose on the Loose*, Fredric Winkowski; *From Grandmamma—With Love*, Kristen Goetters; *Greetings from Camp Wickawac*, Tyrone Geter; *Blue Ribbon Beagle*, Jane McCreary; Lou Vaccaro, *Are We Still Friends?*, Gail Piazza; *Flying Colors*, Colin Bootman; *Storm at Rugged Point*, Ron Himler; *How Do Your Vegetables Grow?*, Frank McShane; Table of Contents, Parent Letter, Signs of Sucess, Gail Piazza.

Photography   *Our Family Vacation*: 3, Ann Duncan/Tom Stack & Associates; 4, Craig K. Lorenz/Photo Researchers; 5, Robert Winslow/Tom Stack & Associates; 6, Randy Trine/DRK; 7, John Eastcott-YVA Momatiuk/DRK; 8, Dick Canby/DRK. *Frogs and Toads in Spring*: 1, Robert C. Hermes/Photo Researchers; 2, Tom McHugh/Photo Researchers; 3t.r., Hugh Spencer/Photo Researchers; 3, Leonard L. Rue/FPG; 4, W. J. Schoonmaker/Photo Researchers; 5, Hal M. Harrison/Photo Researchers; 6-8, Stephen Dalton/Photo Researchers; *Blue Ribbon Beagle*: 1, Animal Images/D. H. Muska; 8, John Lei/OPC. *Are We Still Friends?*: 1-2, Ken Karp/OPC. *Flying Colors*: 8, James Stuart/Allstock.